THE ROLLING STONES

STREET FIGHTING MAN...6   LIKE A ROLLING STONE...10   NOT FADE AWAY...14

SHINE A LIGHT...18   THE SPIDER AND THE FLY...22   I'M FREE...27

WILD HORSES...30   LET IT BLEED...40   DEAD FLOWERS...46   SLIPPING AWAY...35

ANGIE...58   LOVE IN VAIN...50   SWEET VIRGINIA...54   LITTLE BABY...61

Wise Publications / Westminster Music Limited

STREET FIGHTING MAN

Ev'rywhere I hear the sound of marching, charging feet, oh boy.
'Cause summer's here and the time is right for fighting in the street, oh boy.
But what can a poor boy do except to sing for a rock'n'roll band
'Cause in sleepy London Town, there's just no place for a street fighting man! No!

Hey! Think the time is right for a palace revolution.
But where I live the game to play is compromise solution!
Well, then what can a poor boy do except to sing for a rock'n'roll band
'Cause in sleepy London Town, there's just no place for a street fighting man! No!

Hey! Said my name is called Disturbance
I'll shout and scream, I'll kill the king, I'll rail at all his servants.
Well, what can a poor boy do except to sing for a rock'n'roll band
'Cause in sleepy London Town, there's just no place for a street fighting man! No!

What can a poor boy do except to sing for a rock'n'roll band. Well.

LIKE A ROLLING STONE

Once upon a time you dressed so fine,
You threw the bums a dime in your prime, didn't you?
People'd call, say 'beware doll you're bound to fall'
You thought they were all kiddin' you.
You used to laugh about ev'rybody that was hangin' out,
Now you don't talk so loud, now you don't seem so proud
About having to be scrounging for your next meal.

How does it feel, how does it feel,
To be without a home, like a complete unknown,
Like a rolling stone?

You've gone to the finest school all right Miss Lonely,
But you know you only used to get juiced in it.
And nobody's ever taught you how to live on the street
And now you're gonna have to get used to it.
You said you'd never compromise with the mystery tramp,
But now you realise he's not selling you alibis
As you stare into the vacuum of his eyes
And ask him do you want to make a deal?

How does it feel, how does it feel,
To be without a home, like a complete unknown,
Like a rolling stone?

You never turned around to see the frowns on the jugglers and the clowns
When they all come down and did tricks for you
You never understood that it ain't no good
You shouldn't let other people get your kicks for you.
You used to ride on the chrome horse with your diplomat
Who carried on his shoulder a Siamese cat,
Ain't it hard when you discovered that he really wasn't where it's at
After he took from you everything he could steal.

How does it feel, how does it feel,
To be without a home, like a complete unknown,
Like a rolling stone?

NOT FADE AWAY

I want to tell you how it's gonna be.
You're gonna give your love to me.
I'm gonna love you night and day.
Love is love and not fade away.
Well, love is love and not fade away.

My love's bigger than a Cadillac.
I try to show it then you drive me back.
Your love for me has got to be real.
I want you to know just how I feel.
Love a-real not fade away.
Well, love a-real and not fade away.

Princess on the steeple and all the pretty people drinkin', thinkin'
They've got it made.
Exchanging all kinds of precious gifts and things
But you'd better lift your diamond ring, you'd better pawn it babe,
You used to be so amused at Napoleon in rags and the language that he used
Got to him now, he calls you, you can't refuse
When you got nothing, you got nothing to lose,
You're invisible now, you got no secrets to conceal.

I'm gonna tell you how it's gonna be.
You're gonna give your love to me.
Love will last more than one day.
Well, love is love and not fade away.
Well, love is love and not fade away.
Well, love is love and not fade away.
No love is love and not fade away.
Not fade away.

How does it feel, how does it feel,
To be without a home, like a complete unknown,
Like a rolling stone?

I'M FREE

I'm free to do what I want any old time.
I'm free to do what I want any old time.

So love me, hold me, love me, hold me,
I'm free any old time to get what I want.

I'm free to sing my song tho' it is out of time.
I'm free to sing my song tho' it is out of time.

So love me, hold me, love me, hold me,
I'm free any old time to get what I want.

Love me, hold me, love me, hold me.
But I'm free any old time to get what I want.

I'm free to choose what I please any old time.
I'm free to choose who I please any old time.

So love me, hold me, love me, hold me,
I'm free any old time to get what I want.
Yes, I am.

WILD HORSES

Childhood living is easy to do.
The things you wanted, I bought them for you.
Graceless lady, you know who I am.
You know I can't let you slide through my hands.

Wild horses couldn't drag me away.
Wild, wild horses couldn't drag me away.

I watched you suffer a dull aching pain.
Now you decided to show me the same.
No sweeping exits or off-stage lines
Could make me feel bitter or treat you unkind.

Wild horses couldn't drag me away.
Wild, wild horses couldn't drag me away.

I know I've dreamed you a sin and a lie.
I have my freedom, but I don't have much time.
Faith has been broken, tears must be cried.
Let's do some living after we die.

Wild horses couldn't drag me away.
Wild, wild horses, we'll ride them some day.

SHINE A LIGHT

Saw you stretched out in Room Ten-O-Nine
With a smile on your face and a tear right in your eye.
Couldn't see to get a line on you, my sweet honey love.
Berber jew'lry jangling down the street,
Make you shut your eyes at ev'ry woman that you meet.
Could not seem to get a high on you, my sweet honey love.

May the good Lord shine a light on you,
Make every song your favourite tune.
May the good Lord shine a light on you,
Warm like the evening sun.

Well, you're drunk in the alley, baby, with your clothes all torn
And your late night friends leave you in the cold grey dawn.
Just seemed too many files on you, I just can't brush them off.
Angels beating all their wings in time,
With smiles on their faces and a gleam right in their eyes.
Thought I heard one sigh for you, come on up, come on up, now, come on up now.

THE SPIDER AND THE FLY

Sittin', thinkin', sinkin', drinkin' wond'ring what I'd do when I'm thru tonight.
Smoking, moping, maybe just hopin' some little girl will pass on by.
Don't wanna be alone but I love my girl at home.
I remember what she said

She said 'My, my, my don't tell lies. Keep fidelity in your head.
My, my, my, don't tell lies. When you're done you should go to bed.
Don't say Hi, like a spider to a fly.
Jump right ahead and you're dead.'

Sit up, fed up, low down, go 'round down to the bar at the place I'm at.
Sitting, drinking, superfic'ly thinking about the rinsed-out blonde to my left,
Then I said 'Hi' like a spider to a fly,
Remembering what my little girl said.

She was common, flirty, she looked about thirty.
I would have run away but I was on my own.
She told me later, she's a machine operator,
She said she liked the way I held the microphone.
I said 'My, my' like the spider to the fly,
'Jump right ahead in my web'.

DEAD FLOWERS

Well when you're sitting there in your silk upholstered chair,
Talking to some rich folks that you know.
Well I hope you won't see me in my ragged company,
For you know I could never be alone.

Take me down little Suzie, won't you take me down,
I know you think you're the queen of the underground
And you can send me dead flowers every morning.
Send me dead flowers by the mail
Send me dead flowers to my wedding
And I won't forget to put roses on your grave.

Well when you're sitting back in your long pink cadillac,
Making bets on Kentucky Derby Day.
I'll be in my basement room with a needle and a spoon,
And another girl, to take my pain away.

Take me down little Suzie, won't you take me down,
I know you think you're the queen of the underground
And you can send me dead flowers every morning.
Send me dead flowers by the mail
Send me dead flowers to my wedding
And I won't forget to put roses on your grave.

Take me down little Suzie, won't you take me down,
I know you think you're the queen of the underground
And you can send me dead flowers every morning.
Send me dead flowers by the US mail
Say it with dead flowers to my wedding
And I won't forget to put roses on your grave.
No, I won't forget to put roses on your grave.

LET IT BLEED

Well we all need someone we can lean on
And if you want to you can lean on me.
Yeah we all need someone we can lean on,
And if you want to you can lean on me.

She said my breasts they will always be open,
Baby you can rest your weary head right on me.
And there will always be a space in my parking lot
When you need a little Coke and sympathy.

Well we all need someone we can dream on
And if you want to you can dream on me.
Yeah we all need someone we can cream on,
And if you want to you can cream on me.

I was dreaming of a steel guitar engagement,
When you drank my health in scented jasmine tea.
And you knifed me in my dirty, filthy basement
With that jaded faded junky nurse what company.

Well we all need someone we can feed on
And if you want to you can feed on me.
Yeah we all need (take my arms,) someone (take my leg,)
we can cream on (oh, baby don't you take my head.)
And if you want to you can cream on me.

Get it on rider, get it on rider,
Get it on rider, you can bleed all over me.
Get it on rider, get it on rider,
Get it on rider, you can bleed all over me.

We all need someone we can bleed on
And if you want to you can bleed on me.

SLIPPING AWAY

Babe it's just another dream that's slipping away.
Each time that I go to sleep, it seems that I'm dying away.
Just as you have touched my heart babe I wake and we're apart.
Slipping away.

Babe it's just another day that's slipping away.
Each time that I draw a breath, it seems it's dying away.
Well first the sun and then the moon, one of them will be round soon.
Slipping away, slipping away.

Just as you have touched my heart babe I wake and we're apart.
Slipping away, slipping away, slipping away.

All I want is ecstasy, but I ain't getting much,
Getting off on misery it seems I've lost my touch.

Babe it's just another song but it's dying away.
Babe we didn't sing it long 'cause it's fading away.
Well first the sun and then the moon, one of them will be round soon.
Slipping away, slipping away, slipping away.
Slipping away, slipping away.

LITTLE BABY

You go and I'll come with you little baby,
You go and I'll come with you little baby,
You go and I'll come with you,
You bet your life that I can't quit ya,
You go and I'll come with you little baby.

You go to court and I'll come along,
You go to jail and I'll blow your bond,
You get time, I tell ya what I'll do
I'll stay outside and wait for you.

You go and I'll come with you little baby,
You go and I'll come with you little baby,
You go and I'll come with you,
You bet your life that I'll walk with ya,
You go and I'll come with you little baby.

You go to church and I'll go there too,
You go to work, I'll tell ya what I'll do,
You get paid, but I hold the money,
Be right there behind you honey.

You go and I'll come with you little baby,
You go and I'll come with you little baby,
You go and I'll come with you,
You bet your life that I won't quit ya,
You go and I'll come with you little baby.

You get the fares and I'll go the show,
You get the horses, I'll pick up the dough,
You work hard, it'll hurt my pride,
I'll be right there by your side.

You go and I'll come with you little baby,
You go and I'll come with you little baby,
You go and I'll come with you,
You bet your life that I'll walk with ya,
You go and I'll come with you little baby,
Little baby, little baby.

ANGIE

Oh Angie, oh Angie when will those dark clouds disappear.
Angie Angie where will it lead us from here.
With no loving in our souls and no money in our coats
You can't say we're satisfied,
But Angie Angie you can't say we never tried.

Angie you're beautiful but ain't it time we said goodbye.
Angie I still love you remember all those nights we cried.
All the dreams we held so close seemed to all go up in smoke.
Let me whisper in your ear
Angie Angie where will it lead us from here.

Oh Angie don't you weep ah your kisses still taste sweet.
I hate that sadness in your eyes,
But Angie Angie ain't it time we said goodbye.

With no loving in our souls and no money in our coats
You can't say were satisfied,
But Angie I still love you baby
Everywhere I look I see your eyes
There ain't a woman that comes close to you
Come on baby dry your eyes
But Angie Angie ain't it good to be alive
Angie Angie they can't say we never tried.

LOVE IN VAIN

Well I followed her to the station with a suitcase in my hand
Yeah and I followed her up to the station with a suitcase in my hand.
Yeah and it's hard to tell, it's hard to tell, it's hard to tell,
All your love's in vain.

When the train come in the station and I looked her in the eye,
When the train come in the station and I looked her in the eye.
Yeah and I felt so sad and lonesome I hang my head and cry.

When the train left the station it had two lights on behind,
When the train had left the station it had two lights on behind.
Yeah the blue light was my baby and the red light was my mind.

SWEET VIRGINIA

Wadin' through the waste stormy winter,
And there's not a friend to help you through.
Tryin' to stop the waves behind your eye-balls,
Drop your reds, drop your greens and blues.
Thank you for your wine, California,
Thank you for your sweet and bitter fruits.
Yes I got the desert in my toe-nail
And I hid the speed inside my shoe.

But come on, come on down sweet Virginia,
Come on, honey child, I beg of you.
Come on, come on down, you got it in you.
Got to scrape that shit right off your shoes.

Come on, come on down sweet Virginia,
Come on, honey child, I beg of you.
Come on, come on down, you got it in you.
Got to scrape that shit right off your shoes.

Mod. Rock

Ev - 'ry-where I hear the sound of march-ing, charg-ing feet, Oh, Boy. 'Cause

sum-mer's here and the time is right for fight-ing in the street, Oh, Boy. But

what can a poor boy do ex - cept to sing for a Rock'N'Roll Band 'cause in sleep-y Lon - don

Town, There's just no place for Street Fight-ing Man! _____ No!

Hey! Think the time is right for a Pal-ace Rev-o-lu-tion._____ But

where I live the game to play is Com-pro-mise So-lu-tion!_____ Well, Then

What can a poor boy do ex - cept to sing for a Rock'N'Roll Band 'Cause in

sleep - y Lon - don Town there's just no place for Street Fight-ing Man! ____

No!

Hey! Said my name is called Dis - turb - ance ____ I'll shout and scream, I'll

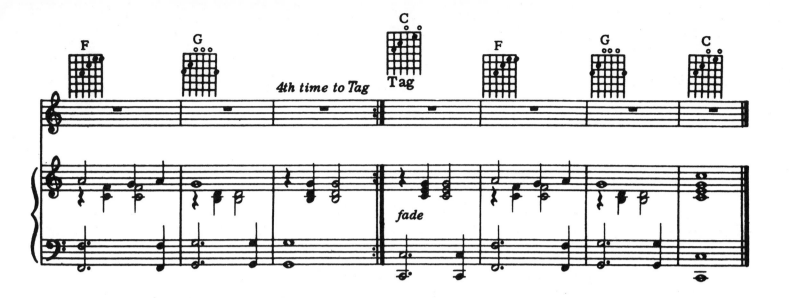

Verse 2. You've gone to the finest school all right Miss Lonely,
But you know you only used to get
Juiced in it.
And nobody's ever taught you how to live on the street
And now you're gonna have to get
Used to it.
You said you'd never compromise
With the mystery tramp, but now you realize
He's not selling any alibis
As you stare into the vacuum of his eyes
And ask him do you want to
Make a deal?

Refrain:

Verse 3. You never turned around to see the frowns on the jugglers and the clowns
When they all come down
And did tricks for you
You never understood that it ain't no good
You shouldn't let other people
Get your kicks for you.
You used to ride on the chrome horse with your diplomat
Who carried on his shoulder a Siamese cat,
Ain't it hard when you discovered that
He really wasn't where it's at
After he took from you everything
He could steal.

Refrain:

Verse 4. Princess on the steeple
And all the pretty people're drinkin', thinkin'
That they got it made.
Exchanging all kinds of precious gifts and things
But you'd better lift your diamond ring,
You'd better pawn it babe,
You used to be so amused
At Napoleon in rags and the language that he used
Go to him now, he calls you, you can't refuse
When you got nothing, you got nothing to lose,
You're invisible now, you got no secrets
To conceal.

Refrain:

Well, love a-real_ and not fade a-way._

Harmonica

Slowly, with a beat
Verse

18

Chorus

THE SPIDER AND THE FLY

WORDS & MUSIC BY MICK JAGGER & KEITH RICHARDS

Sit-tin' think-in' sink-in' drink-in' won - d'ring what I'd do__ when I'm

thru__ to - night.__ Smok-ing, mop-ing, may-be just hop-in'

To Coda ⊕

some lit - tle girl__ will pass on by.__ Don't wan - na be a - lone but I

love my girl at home. I re - mem - ber what she said__ She said,

"My,__ my,__ my don't tell__ lies. Keep fi - del - i - ty in your head.

My, my, my,__ don't tell__ lies.

When you're done you should go to bed.___   Don't say Hi,___ like the

spi - der to a fly.   Jump right a - head and you're dead."___

*Guitar solo 1st time
Harmonica solo 2nd time

Verse 2:
Sit up, fed up, low down, go 'round down to the bar at the place I'm at.
Sitting, drinking, superfic'ly thinking about the rinsed-out blonde on my left,
Then I said "Hi" like a spider to a fly,
Remembering what my little girl said.
To Guitar Solo

Verse 3:
She was common, flirty, she looked about thirty.
I would have run away but I was on my own.
She told me later, she's a machine operator,
She said she liked the way I held the microphone.
I said "My, My," like the spider to the fly,
"Jump right ahead in my web."
To Harmonica Solo

*Harmony vocal 8va.

*Harmony vocal 8va.
**8va if played by guitar.

Verse 3:
I'm free to choose what I please any old time.
I'm free to please who I choose and old time.
To Chorus:

Moderately slow ♩ = 88

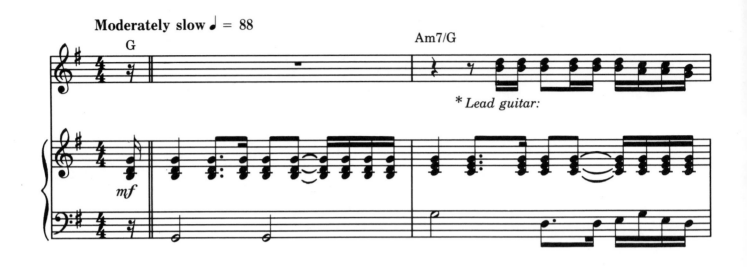

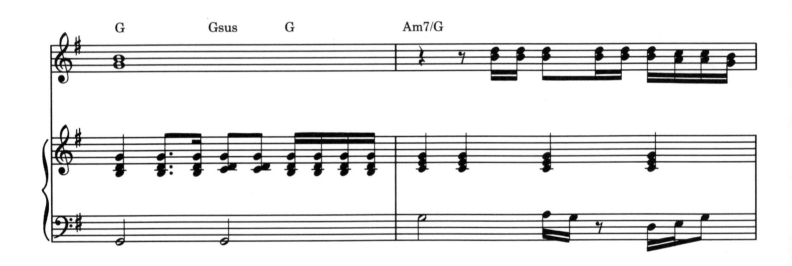

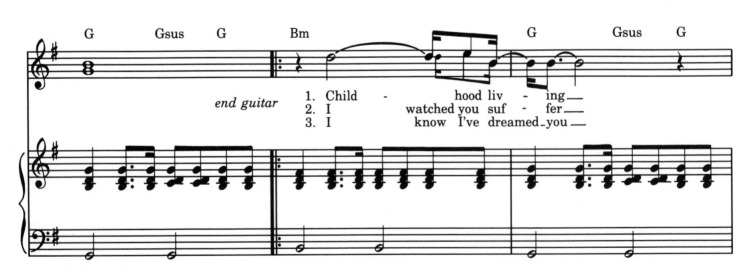

1. Child - hood liv - ing
2. I watched you suf - fer
3. I know I've dreamed you

8va if played by Guitar.

8va if played by Guitar.

8va if played by Guitar.

♩=126

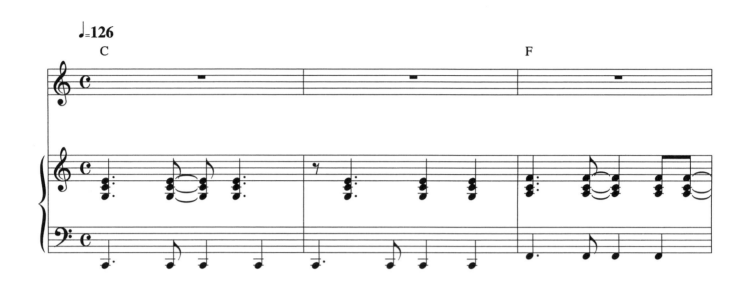

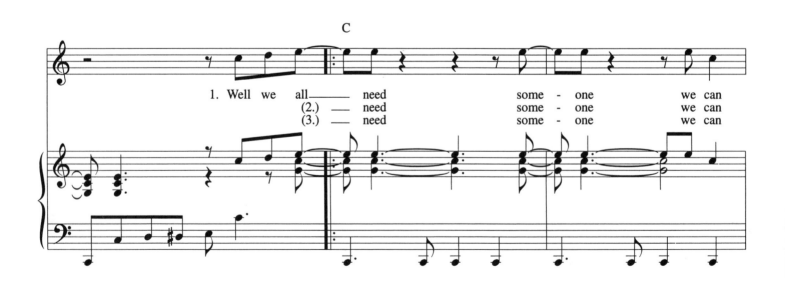

1. Well we all____ need some - one we can
(2.) ____ need some - one we can
(3.) ____ need some - one we can

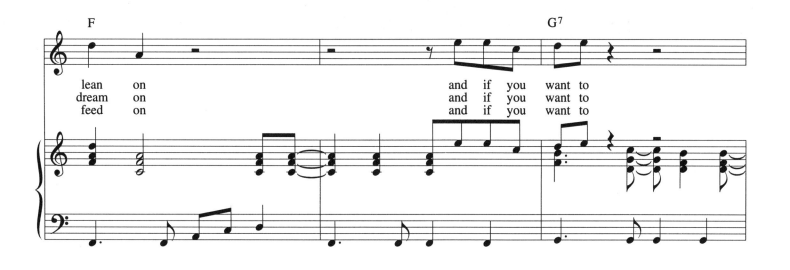

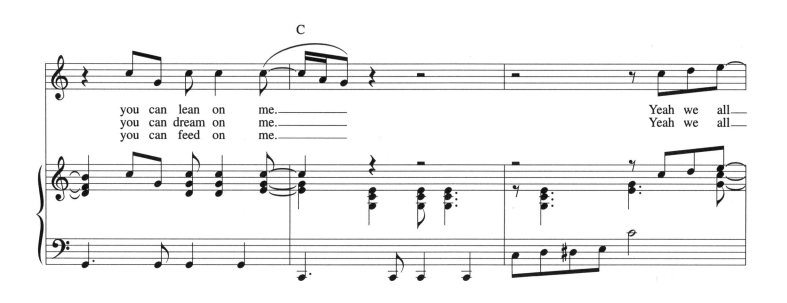

And there will al - ways__ be a space__ in my
And you knifed me__ in my dir - ty fil - thy

park - ing lot
base - ment

when you need__ a lit - tle
with that ja - ded fa - ded

Coke__ and sym - pa - thy.__
jun - ky nurse__ what com - pa - ny.

Will we all__

3.

LOVE IN VAIN
WORDS & MUSIC BY ROBERT JOHNSON
ARRANGED & ADAPTED BY MICK JAGGER & KEITH RICHARDS

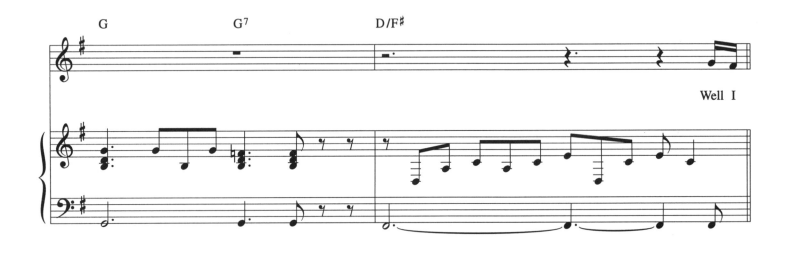

SWEET VIRGINIA

WORDS & MUSIC BY MICK JAGGER & KEITH RICHARDS

Very slow tempo ♩= 80

ba - by,___ You go and I'll___

come with you, you bet your life that

I___ can't quit___ ya,
I'll___ walk with___ ya,
I___ won't quit___ ya,
I'll___ walk with___ ya,

you go and I'll___ come with___ you lit - tle ba - by.___

You go to court___ and I'll come a - long,___ you go to jail___ and
You go to church___ and I'll go there too,___ you go to work, I'll tell ya___
You get the fares___ and I'll go the show,___ you bet the horses,

3° D.%. al Coda

Coda

Repeat ad lib. to fade

Exclusive Distributors:
Music Sales Limited
8/9 Frith Street, London W1V 5TZ, England.
Music Sales Pty Limited
120 Rothschild Avenue, Rosebery, NSW 2018, Australia.

Order No. WM400103
ISBN 0-7119-5560-3
This book © Copyright 1995 by Wise Publications / Westminster Music Limited

Printed in the United Kingdom by
J.B. Offset Printers (Marks Tey) Limited, Marks Tey, Essex.

Your Guarantee of Quality:
As publishers, we strive to produce every book to the highest commercial standards.
Whilst endeavouring to retain the original running order of the recorded album, the book has been
carefully designed to minimise awkward page turns and to make playing from it a real pleasure.
Particular care has been given to specifying acid-free, neutral-sized paper made from pulps which have not been elemental chlorine bleached.
This pulp is from farmed sustainable forests and was produced with special regard for the environment.
Throughout, the printing and binding have been planned to ensure a sturdy, attractive publication which should give years of enjoyment.
If your copy fails to meet our high standards, please inform us and we will gladly replace it.

Music Sales' complete catalogue describes thousands of titles and is available
in full colour sections by subject, direct from Music Sales Limited.
Please state your areas of interest and send a cheque/postal order for £1.50 for postage to:
Music Sales Limited, Newmarket Road, Bury St. Edmunds, Suffolk IP33 3YB.

Visit the Internet Music Shop at
http://www.musicsales.co.uk